Follow Up Activities

CONTENTS

Points scored by Olympic Decathlon winners		
Year	**Winner**	**Points**
1960	Rafer Johnson (USA)	8 392
1964	Willi Holdorf (Germany)	7 887
1968	Bill Toomey (USA)	8 193
1972	Nikolai Avilov (Russia)	8 454
1976	Bruce Jenner (USA)	8 617
1980	Daley Thompson (Great Britain)	8 495
1984	Daley Thompson (Great Britain)	8 798
1988	Christian Schenk (Germany)	8 488
1992	Robert Zmelik (Czechoslovakia)	8 611
1996	Dan O'Brien (USA)	8 824

Write these winners' points in figures, then words.

Thompson (1984) _8798_ eight   thousand, ...

....

Thompson (1980) ....

....

Johnson (1960) ....

....

Jenner (1976) ....

....

Holdorf (1964) ....

....

Name ....

Use addition **or** subtraction to solve the problem.
Then use the **inverse** operation to check the answer.
Show your working both times.

How much more is than ?	What is the difference in price between 👟 and 🏀 ? ....
Jade has £14. How much more does she need to buy ?	Ellie had £50. How much did she have left after she bought 👟 ? ....

Relating addition and subtraction
(Follows *Giant Discussion Book* page 3.)

3

Top-selling computer games (monthly sales)

	MAZE RUNNER	ROAD RACER	SPACE TREK	SPINNER
October	246	127	153	168
November	182	257	178	165

1. Calculate the difference in sales in **October** between
   Maze Runner and each of the other games.

Road Racer	**Space Trek**	**Spinner**
246 −127		

2. Calculate the difference in sales in **November** between
   Road Racer and each of the other games.

Space Trek	**Maze Runner**	**Spinner**

4

Using informal pencil and paper methods (−)
(Follows *Giant Discussion Book* page 4.)

Name ....

Each of these children measured one giant step.
Write the missing numbers on their worksheets.

Adam

I giant step: ___80___ cm

2 giant steps: _____ cm

      = ___ m _____ cm

      = _____ m

3 giant steps: _____ cm

      = ___ m _____ cm

      = _____ m

Kim

I giant step: ___75___ cm

2 giant steps: _____ cm

      = ___ m _____ cm

      = _____ m

3 giant steps: _____ cm

      = ___ m _____ cm

      = _____ m

Lauren

I giant step: ___105___ cm

2 giant steps: _____ cm

      = ___ m _____ cm

      = _____ m

3 giant steps: _____ cm

      = ___ m _____ cm

      = _____ m

Jack

I giant step: ___85___ cm

2 giant steps: _____ cm

      = ___ m _____ cm

      = _____ m

3 giant steps: _____ cm

      = ___ m _____ cm

      = _____ m

Name ....

Write the length and width of each frame:

- in millimetres
- as a decimal fraction of one metre.

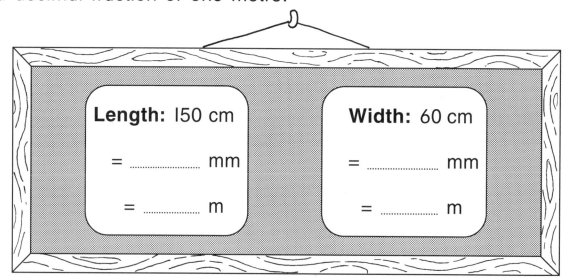

Length: 150 cm

= .... mm

= .... m

Width: 60 cm

= .... mm

= .... m

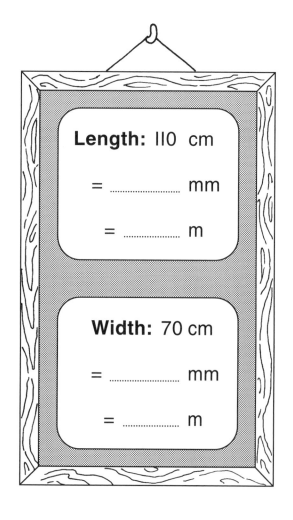

Length: 110 cm

= .... mm

= .... m

Width: 70 cm

= .... mm

= .... m

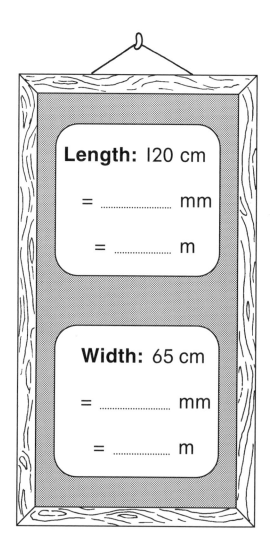

Length: 120 cm

= .... mm

= .... m

Width: 65 cm

= .... mm

= .... m

Using decimal fractions of one metre
(Follows *Giant Discussion Book* page 6.)

Name ....

To solve each problem, calculate the **perimeter** of the rectangle.
Show your working.

What length of fencing would
this garden need?

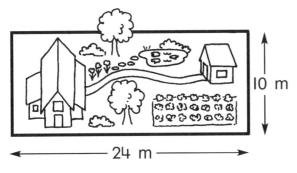

10 m

24 m

....

How far is it around the edge
of the swimming pool?

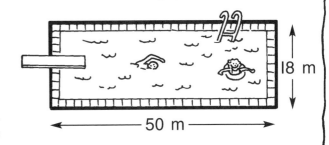

18 m

50 m

....

How long is the ribbon
around the cake?

52 cm

26 cm

....

To frame the painting, what
length of wood should I buy?

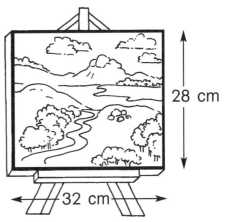

28 cm

32 cm

....

Calculating the perimeter of rectangles
(Follows *Giant Discussion Book* page 7.)

7

Name ....

1. Colour the triangles:
   - **red** for **equilateral** triangles
   - **yellow** for **isosceles** triangles
   - **blue** for **right-angled** triangles.

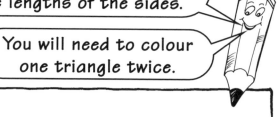

Use a ruler to help compare the lengths of the sides.

You will need to colour one triangle twice.

2. Mark the angles:
   - ✗ for the **right-angle** in each right-angled triangle
   - ✓ for the **equal angles** in each isosceles triangle.

Recognise right-angled, equilateral and isosceles triangles
(Follows *Giant Discussion Book* page 8.)

Name ....

1. Loop each of these points on the ship.

    (1,3) red   (8,5) green   (13,3) blue

    (11,4) yellow   (2,1) orange   (4,3) purple

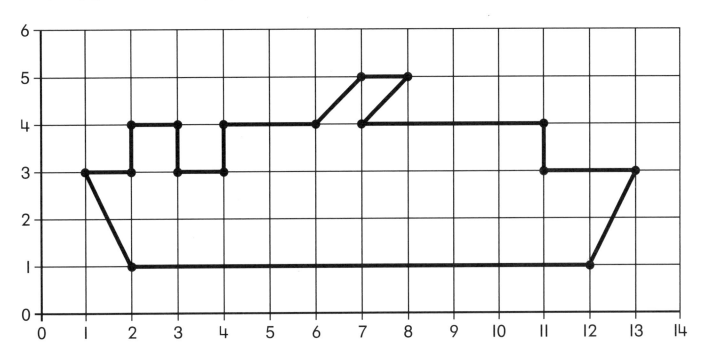

2. Draw a square window on the ship.
   Write the points for each corner of the square.

  (.......... , ...)   (.......... , ...)   (.......... , ...)   (.......... , ...)

3. Fill in the missing points used to draw the ship.
   (List them in order.)

(1,3)   (2,3)   (2,4)   (.......... , ...)   (.......... , ...)

(.......... , ...)   (.......... , ...)   (.......... , ...)   (.......... , ...)

(.......... , ...)   (.......... , ...)   (.......... , ...)   (.......... , ...)

(.......... , ...)   (.......... , ...)   (.......... , ...)   (1,3)

Name ....

Use a different colour for each step.

I. Colour the grid to make the square 'grow'.
Complete an addition sentence after each step.

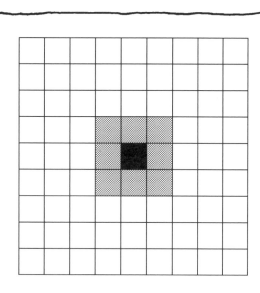

Starting number: 1

_1_ + _8_ = _9_

_9_ + _____ = _____

_____ + _____ = _____

_____ + _____ = _____

2. What patterns do you see? ....

....

....

3. Keep these patterns going.

Starting number: 4

_4_ + _12_ = _____

_____ + _____ = _____

_____ + _____ = _____

_____ + _____ = _____

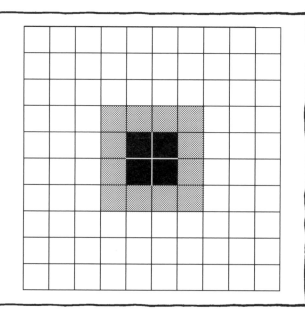

4. Write the missing square numbers.

Recognising number patterns
(Follows *Giant Discussion Book* page 10.)

Name ....

Write the missing numbers.

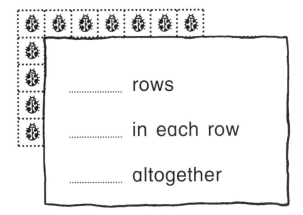

.... rows

.... in each row

.... altogether

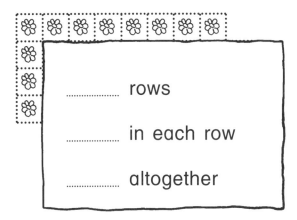

.... rows

.... in each row

.... altogether

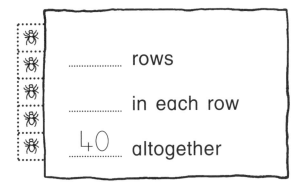

.... rows

.... in each row

40 altogether

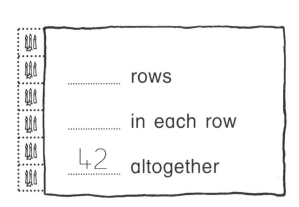

.... rows

.... in each row

42 altogether

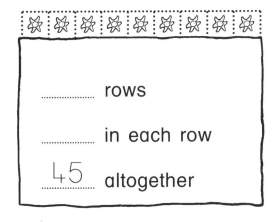

.... rows

.... in each row

45 altogether

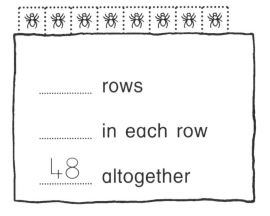

.... rows

.... in each row

48 altogether

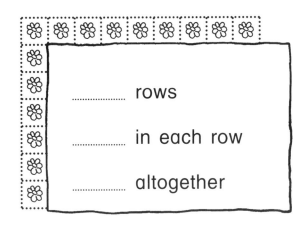

.... rows

.... in each row

.... altogether

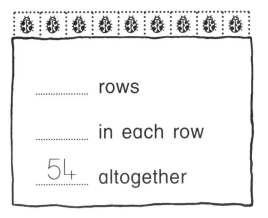

.... rows

.... in each row

54 altogether

Relating multiplication and division
(Follows *Giant Discussion Book* page 11.)

11

Use the children's methods to multiply by 4.

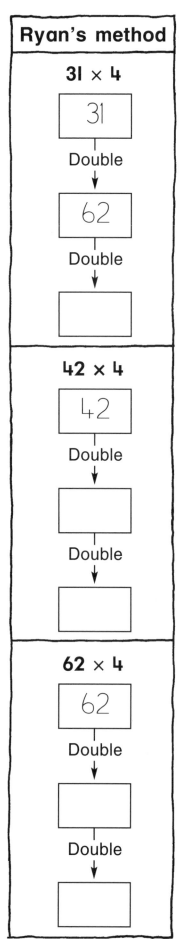

Ryan's method

31 × 4

31
↓ Double
62
↓ Double
[ ]

42 × 4

42
↓ Double
[ ]
↓ Double
[ ]

62 × 4

62
↓ Double
[ ]
↓ Double
[ ]

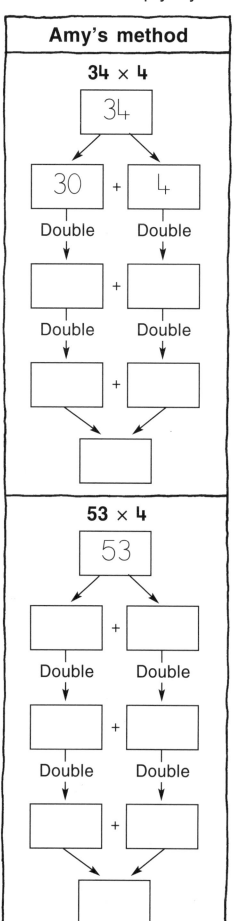

Amy's method

34 × 4

34
↙ ↘
30 + 4
↓ Double ↓ Double
[ ] + [ ]
↓ Double ↓ Double
[ ] + [ ]
↘ ↙
[ ]

53 × 4

53
↙ ↘
[ ] + [ ]
↓ Double ↓ Double
[ ] + [ ]
↓ Double ↓ Double
[ ] + [ ]
↘ ↙
[ ]

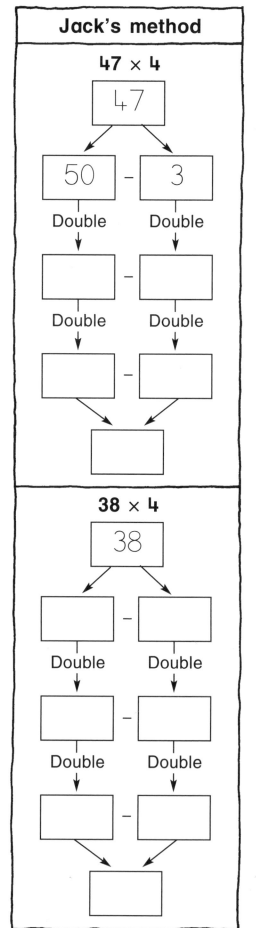

Jack's method

47 × 4

47
↙ ↘
50 − 3
↓ Double ↓ Double
[ ] − [ ]
↓ Double ↓ Double
[ ] − [ ]
↘ ↙
[ ]

38 × 4

38
↙ ↘
[ ] − [ ]
↓ Double ↓ Double
[ ] − [ ]
↓ Double ↓ Double
[ ] − [ ]
↘ ↙
[ ]

Using doubling strategies
(Follows *Giant Discussion Book* page 12.)

Name ....

Loop the fraction of sweets on the tray.
Complete the fraction sentence.
Write the division sentence that helps you find the answer.

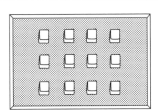

$\frac{1}{4}$ of 12 is ....

12 ÷ 4 =

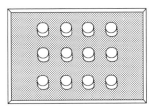

$\frac{1}{3}$ of 12 is ....

....

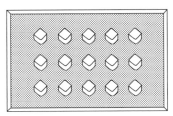

$\frac{1}{3}$ of 15 is ....

....

$\frac{1}{4}$ of 8 is ....

....

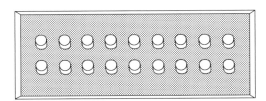

$\frac{1}{2}$ of 18 is ....

....

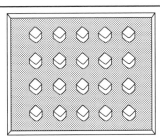

$\frac{1}{4}$ of 20 is ....

....

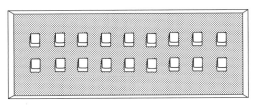

$\frac{1}{3}$ of 18 is ....

....

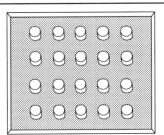

$\frac{1}{5}$ of 20 is ....

....

Relating fractions to division
(Follows *Giant Discussion Book* page 13.)

13

Name ....

Count in steps of one quarter. Colour the pies to match.
Write the fractions and mixed numbers.

⬭ = one whole	Fractions	Whole or Mixed Numbers
⬭ ⬭ ⬭	$\frac{1}{4}$	
⬭ ⬭ ⬭		
⬭ ⬭ ⬭		
⬭ ⬭ ⬭	$\frac{4}{4}$	1
⬭ ⬭ ⬭	$\frac{5}{4}$	$1\frac{1}{4}$
⬭ ⬭ ⬭		
⬭ ⬭ ⬭		
⬭ ⬭ ⬭		
⬭ ⬭ ⬭		
⬭ ⬭ ⬭		
⬭ ⬭ ⬭		
⬭ ⬭ ⬭		

Recognising 'top heavy' fractions and mixed numbers
(Follows *Giant Discussion Book* page 14.)

Name ....

For each **continent**, calculate the number of stamps Lucy and Sam have altogether.

Show your working in the space below the table.

Stamps in our collections						
	Africa	**Asia**	**Australia**	**Europe**	**North America**	**South America**
Lucy	123	85	136	248	324	78
Sam	156	134	148	177	278	122
Total						

Africa	Asia	Australia

Europe	North America	South America

1. Use **red** to colour the **a.m.** section of the timeline.
   Use **blue** to colour the **p.m.** section.

2. Write these times from the timeline.

A	Wake up	6:30 a.m.
B	Leave for school	
C	Maths	
D	Science	
E	Lunch	
F	Art	
G	Leave school	
H	Arrive home	
I	Play outside	
J	Dinner	
K	Read	
L	Bedtime	

3. Calculate the difference (in hours, or hours and minutes) between these pairs of times.

A	and	**B**	
C	and	**D**	
D	and	**E**	
E	and	**G**	

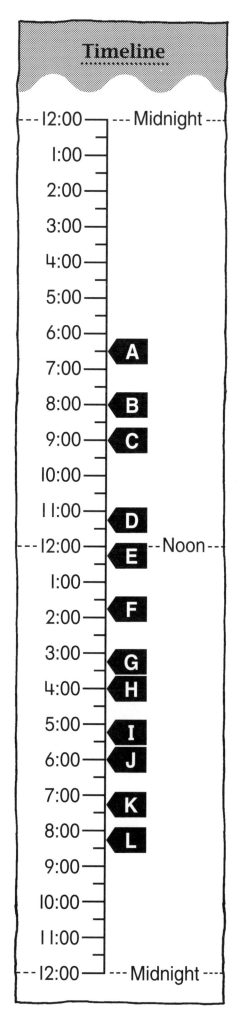

16 **Using a.m. and p.m.**
(Follows *Giant Discussion Book* page 16.)

Name ....

Favourite type of book

Theme	Aaron's survey	Julia's survey
Fantasy	卌 卌	
Humour	卌 卌 I	
Mystery	卌 卌 卌 II	
Adventure	卌 II	
Animal Stories	卌 卌 II	
Science Fiction	卌 IIII	

(Julia's survey pictogram key: 📘 = two votes)

1. How many people **altogether** voted for Science Fiction? ....
   (Note: no one voted in **both** surveys.)

2. Complete this table.

	Aaron's survey	Julia's survey
What was the most popular theme?	....	....
List the themes with more than 10 votes.	....	....
What is the difference between the votes for the most popular and least popular theme?	.... − .... = ...	.... − .... = ...
How many people were surveyed?	....	....

Name ....

1. Find each pair of buildings in the table.
   Tick the box for the building with the **greater** number of steps.

☐ Ostankino Tower
☐ T'ai Chan Temple

☐ Empire State Building
☐ Ostankino Tower

☐ CN Tower
☐ Ostankino Tower

☐ Empire State Building
☐ Sears Tower

☐ Aura Power Station
☐ MAR Power Station

Long flights of stairs	
Location	Steps
Aura Power Station (Norway)	3 715
CN Tower (Canada)	3 642
Empire State Building (USA)	2 908
MAR Power Station (Norway)	3 875
Niesenbahu Funicular Railway (Switzerland)	11 674
Ostankino Tower (Russia)	3 544
Sears Tower (USA)	2 906
T'ai Chan Temple (China)	6 608
Tokyo Tower (Japan)	2 184

2. Copy **both** numbers from the table.
   Write > or < in the box to make a true sentence.

T'ai Chan Temple	□	MAR Power Station	CN Tower	□	Aura Power Station
....		....	....		....
Tokyo Tower	□	Sears Tower	Empire State Building	□	Tokyo Tower
....		....	....		....
Empire State Building	□	Sears Tower	Ostankino Tower	□	Aura Power Station
....		....	....		....

Comparing and ordering numbers
(Follows *Giant Discussion Book* page 18.)

Name ....

1. Write the missing numbers next to the thermometer.

2. What patterns do you see?

   ....

   ....

   ....

   ....

3. Loop the temperature that is **lower**.

   17°C   or   7°C

   17°C   or   −7°C

   −17°C   or   −7°C

   −17°C   or   7°C

4. Write a **negative** temperature that is:

   higher than −11°C

   °C

   lower than 9°C

   between −3°C and 3°C

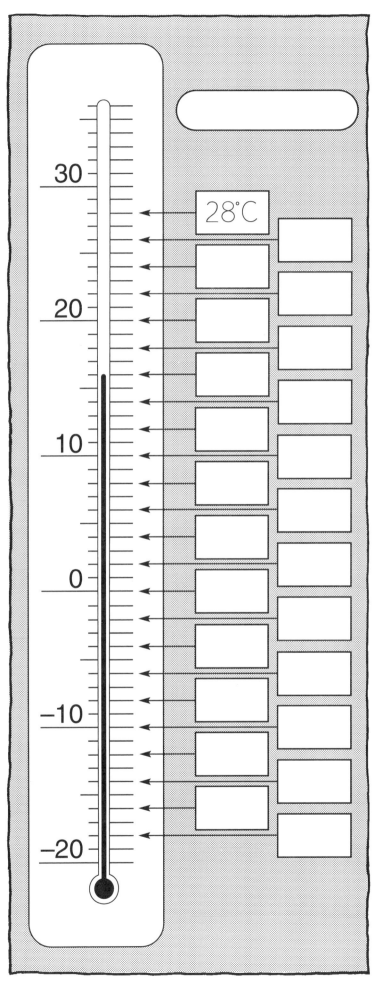

28°C

Name _____

1. Solve these problems. Show your working.

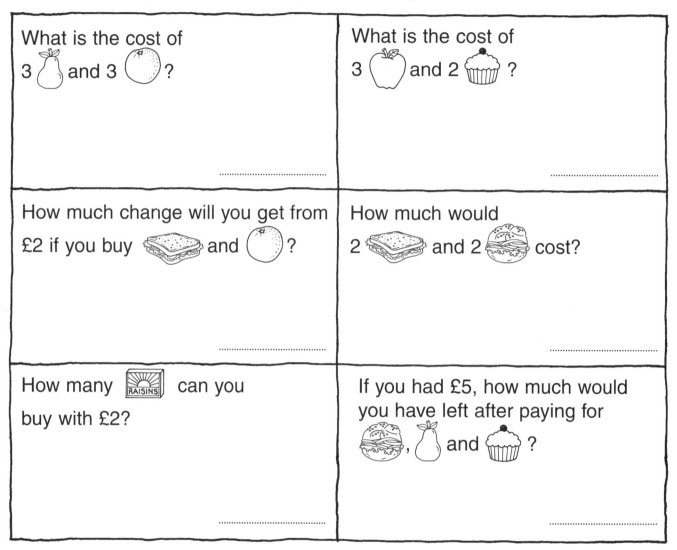

What is the cost of 3 🍐 and 3 🍊 ?	What is the cost of 3 🍎 and 2 🧁 ? ....
How much change will you get from £2 if you buy 🥪 and 🍊 ?	How much would 2 🥪 and 2 🍔 cost? ....
How many RAISINS can you buy with £2?	If you had £5, how much would you have left after paying for 🍔, 🍐 and 🧁 ? ....

2. Draw the lunch you would buy for a family
   of 2 adults and 2 children with £10 to spend.

What is the total cost? .... How much change would they get? ....

Solving real-life problems: money
(Follows *Giant Discussion Book* page 20.)

Name ....

Colour the labels that match the weight shown on the scale.

$2\frac{1}{2}$ kg	250 g	4 g	4.0 kg	3.5 g	3.500 kg
2500 g	2.5 g	4 kg	4000 g	35 kg	3 kg 500 g

$1\frac{1}{2}$ kg	$1\frac{1}{4}$ kg	750 g	$\frac{3}{4}$ kg	0.5 g	$\frac{1}{2}$ kg
1250 g	1.25 kg	34 kg	0.75 g	50 g	500 g

0.1 kg	$\frac{1}{4}$ kg	$1\frac{3}{4}$ kg	1.75 kg	2.5 kg	250 kg
0.25 kg	250 g	1750 kg	175 kg	$2\frac{1}{4}$ kg	2 kg 500 g

Name _____

1. Figure out how many packages of chocolate you would need to buy for each weight in the table.

1 kg	2		
$1\frac{1}{2}$ kg			
$2\frac{1}{2}$ kg			

2. List what you would buy to get the exact amount of chocolate in the Rocky Road recipe.

....

....

Rocky Road

800 g chocolate, melted
600 g raspberry jellies
100 g peanuts (unsalted)
 50 g marshmallows, chopped

3. Answer these questions for **double** the Rocky Road recipe.

List the packages of chocolate you would buy.	How many 150 g packets of raspberry jellies would you need?
How many grams of peanuts would be left over from a $\frac{1}{4}$ kg packet?	What **fraction** of a kilogram more or less than $1\frac{1}{2}$ kg is the amount of chocolate you need?

Solving real-life problems: measurement
(Follows *Giant Discussion Book* page 22.)

Name ....

For some shapes, you will need to use halving to help count the squares.

1. Count and colour the squares in each shape. Write the area.

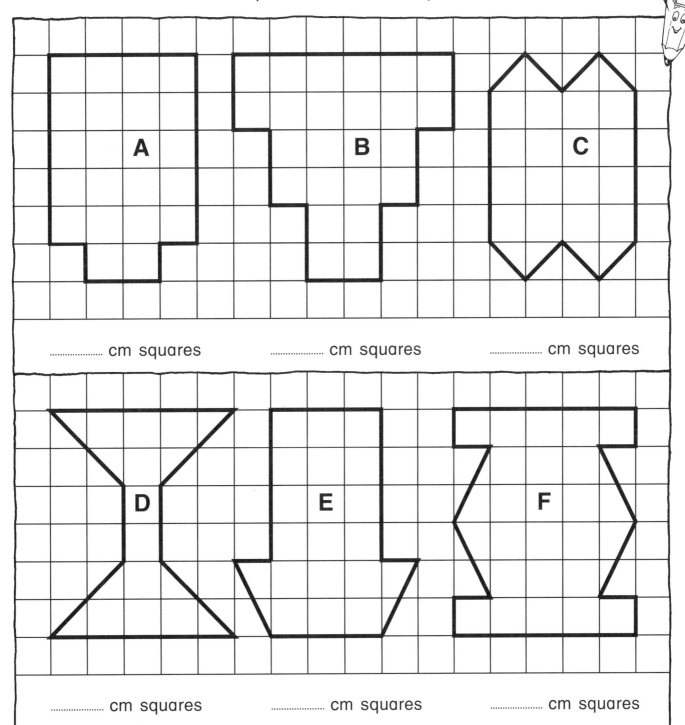

.... cm squares   .... cm squares   .... cm squares

.... cm squares   .... cm squares   .... cm squares

2. Write the letters for these shapes.

The shape with the largest area:	The shape with the smallest area:	Two shapes with the same area: .... and ....

Name ....

To make each 3D shape:
- cut out the net
- fold along the lines
- tape the edges together.

Teacher's note:
Make cardboard copies of this page. You might also want to enlarge the shapes. Tabs could be added (to every second edge) before photocopying the page, but children often find it easier to use tape to join the edges.

Working with simple nets
(Follows *Giant Discussion Book* page 24.)

Name ....

1. Write S, E, W, NE, SE, NW and SW on the compass.
2. Follow the path from the **start**.
   Write on each arrow the direction it is pointing.

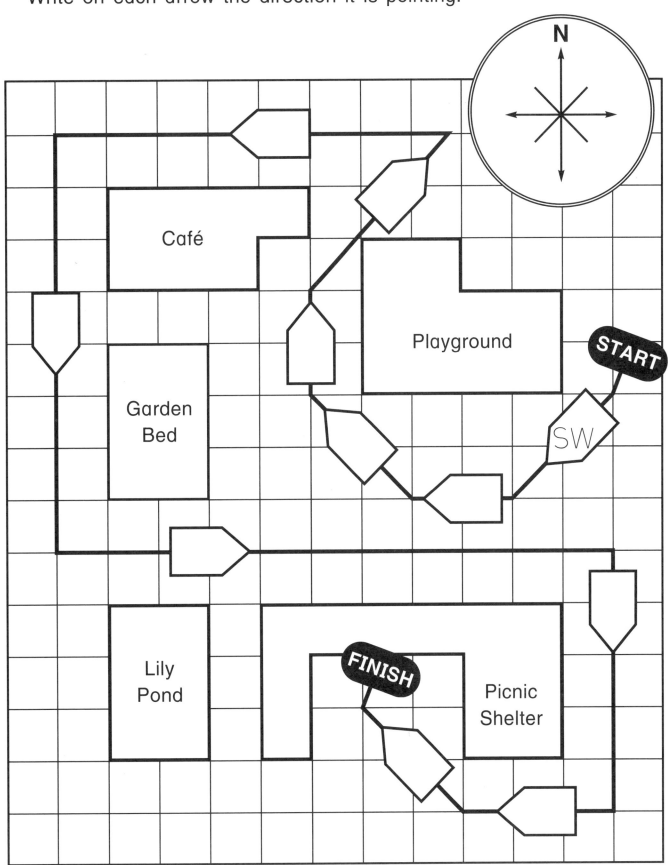

Name ....

Join the stack of cubes to the matching
multiplication sentence. Then fill in the numbers
to help you find the total number of cubes.

You can multiply
the numbers in any
order. Write in the
brackets the two
numbers you
multiply first.

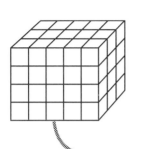 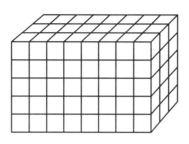 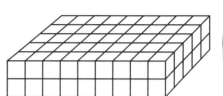

2 × 9 × 5

= (....... × ....) × ....

= .... × ....

= .... cubes

3 × 4 × 5

= (5 × 4) × ....

= .... × ....

= .... cubes

3 × 5 × 8

= (....... × ....) × ....

= .... × ....

= .... cubes

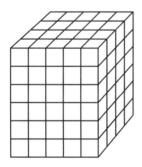 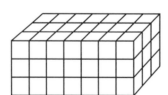 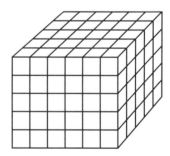

4 × 6 × 5

= (....... × ....) × ....

= .... × ....

= .... cubes

5 × 5 × 6

= (....... × ....) × ....

= .... × ....

= .... cubes

3 × 3 × 7

= (....... × ....) × ....

= .... × ....

= .... cubes

Name ....

Figure out the cost of one CD in each of these packs.

You could use notes and coins to help figure out the answers.

5 CDs
£35

Each CD costs ....

5 CDs
£36

Each CD costs ....

4 CDs
£21

Each CD costs ....

2 CDs
£27

Each CD costs ....

10 CDs
£119

Each CD costs ....

5 CDs
£29

Each CD costs ....

4 CDs
£38

Each CD costs ....

4 CDs
£39

Each CD costs ....

Name _____

Write the answer for the **×10** fact.
Draw one more ◯ and figure out the **×11** answer.
Cross out one ◯ and figure out the **×9** answer.

14 × 10 = _____	14 × 11 = 140 + 14 = _____	14 × 9 = 140 – 14 = _____
⑭ ⑭ ⑭ ⑭ ⑭ ⑭ ⑭ ⑭ ⑭ ⑭	⑭ ⑭ ⑭ ⑭ ⑭ ⑭ ⑭ ⑭ ⑭ ⑭ ⑭	⑭ ⑭ ⑭ ⑭ ⑭ ✗ ⑭ ⑭ ⑭ ⑭ ⑭
27 × 10 = _____	27 × 11 = _____ + 27 = _____	27 × 9 = _____ – 27 = _____
㉗ ㉗ ㉗ ㉗ ㉗ ㉗ ㉗ ㉗ ㉗ ㉗	㉗ ㉗ ㉗ ㉗ ㉗ ㉗ ㉗ ㉗ ㉗ ㉗	㉗ ㉗ ㉗ ㉗ ㉗ ㉗ ㉗ ㉗ ㉗ ㉗
19 × 10 = _____	19 × 11 = _____ + _____ = _____	19 × 9 = _____ – _____ = _____
⑲ ⑲ ⑲ ⑲ ⑲ ⑲ ⑲ ⑲ ⑲ ⑲	⑲ ⑲ ⑲ ⑲ ⑲ ⑲ ⑲ ⑲ ⑲ ⑲	⑲ ⑲ ⑲ ⑲ ⑲ ⑲ ⑲ ⑲ ⑲ ⑲
22 × 10 = _____	22 × 11 = _____ + _____ = _____	22 × 9 = _____ – _____ = _____
㉒ ㉒ ㉒ ㉒ ㉒ ㉒ ㉒ ㉒ ㉒ ㉒	㉒ ㉒ ㉒ ㉒ ㉒ ㉒ ㉒ ㉒ ㉒ ㉒	㉒ ㉒ ㉒ ㉒ ㉒ ㉒ ㉒ ㉒ ㉒ ㉒

Name ....

Use the sketches to help multiply.

Problem	Sketches	Answer
23 × 5	x 20 3 5 [100 ....]	100 + ... = ...
14 × 7	x 10 4 7 [.......... ....]	.... + ... = ...
26 × 3	x .... 3 [.......... ....]	60 + ... = ...
34 × 7	x .... 7 [.......... ....]	.... + ... = ...
24 × 6	x .... [.......... ....]	.... + ... = ...
28 × 4	x .... [.......... ....]	.... + ... = ...

Name ....

1. Colour parts of each shape. Write the fraction coloured.

Colour 3 parts	**Colour 4 parts**	**Colour 5 parts**

2. Loop each fraction. Use:
- **red** for fractions **less than** $\frac{1}{2}$
- **blue** for fractions **equal to** $\frac{1}{2}$
- **green** for fractions **more than** $\frac{1}{2}$.

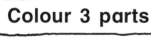
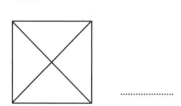
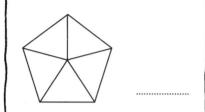
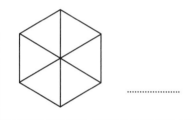
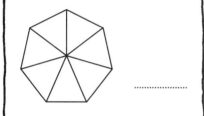
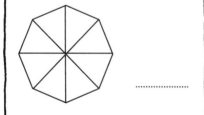
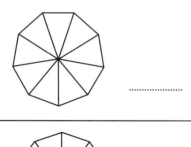
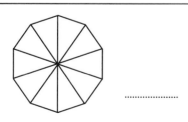

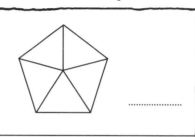
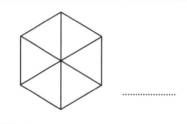
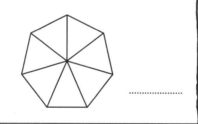
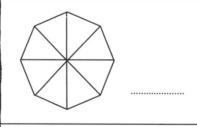
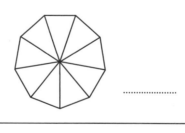

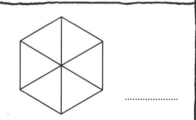

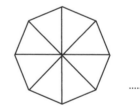
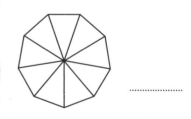
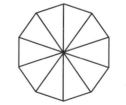

Comparing fractions to one half
(Follows *Giant Discussion Book* page 30.)

Name ....

1. Write each price in £.p notation.
Write each length in metres.
Round each answer to the nearest £ or metre.

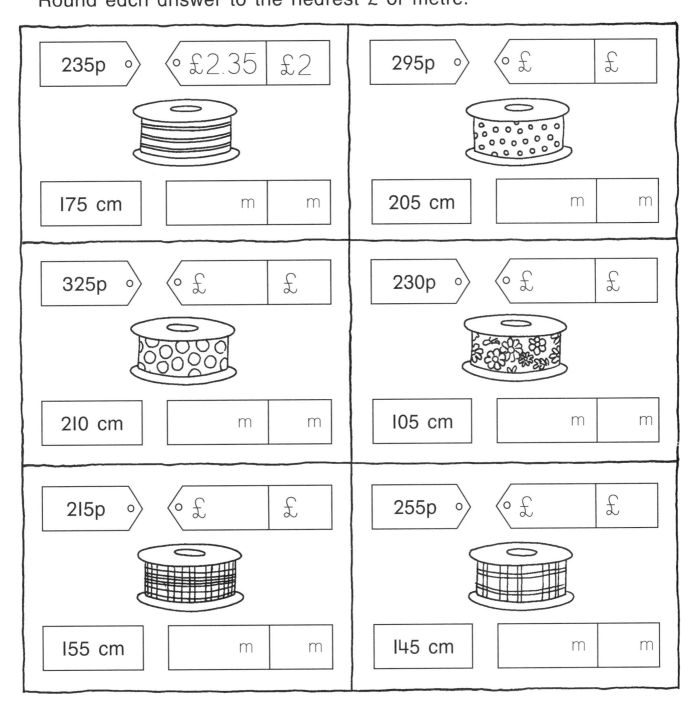

| 235p | £2.35 | £2 |
| 175 cm | m | m |

| 295p | £ | £ |
| 205 cm | m | m |

| 325p | £ | £ |
| 210 cm | m | m |

| 230p | £ | £ |
| 105 cm | m | m |

| 215p | £ | £ |
| 155 cm | m | m |

| 255p | £ | £ |
| 145 cm | m | m |

2. Write the prices in order (cheapest to most expensive).

| £2.15 | | | | | |

3. Write the lengths in order (shortest to longest).

| 1.05 m | | | | | |

Name _____

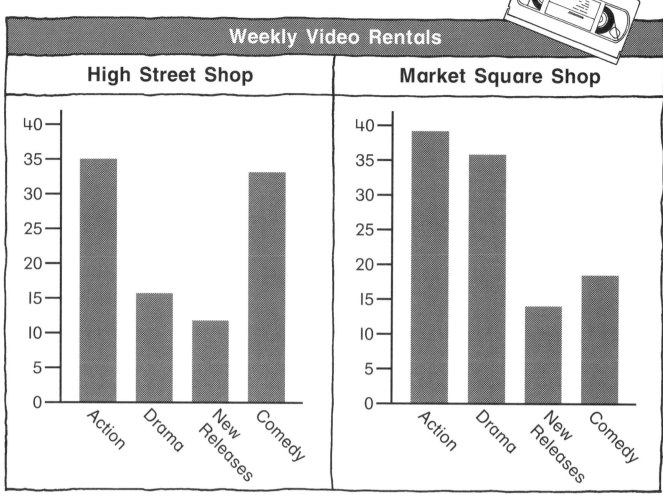

Weekly Video Rentals

| High Street Shop | Market Square Shop |

1. Complete this table. (First write the numbers shown
   by each bar on the graphs. Then figure out the totals.)

	Action	Drama	New Releases	Comedy	Total
High Street Shop					
Market Square Shop					
Total					

2. Complete the sentence to make a word problem
   about the video rentals.

What was the difference between ....

....

....?

Name ....

	Game 1	Game 2
Kurt	81	186
Laura	117	42
Aziz	62	79
Amy	52	123
Owen	104	58
Jamie	91	88

1. Calculate the **total** score for each player.
   Show your working.

Use a near multiple of 10 to help.

Kurt	Laura	Aziz
186 + 80 = ... so 186 + 81 = ...		
Amy	**Owen**	**Jamie**

2. Calculate the **difference** between each player's scores.

Kurt	Laura	Aziz
186 – 80 = ... so 186 – 81 = ...		
Amy	**Owen**	**Jamie**

Adding or subtracting the nearest multiple of 10 and adjusting 33
(Follows *Giant Discussion Book* page 33.)

Name ....

1. Write the missing numbers.
What do you notice?

....

....

2. Use the block pictures to help you subtract. (You could cross out blocks as you take away the tens and units.)

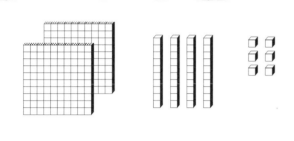

200 + 40 + ... = ...

246 − 23 = ...

$$200 + 40 + 6$$
$$-20 + 3$$

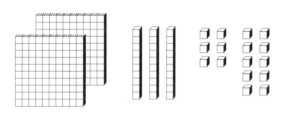

.... + ... + 16 = ...

246 − 28 = ...

$$200 + 30 + 16$$
$$-20 + 8$$

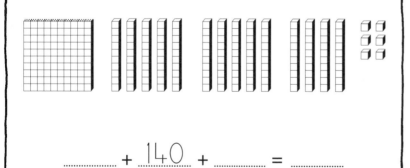

.... + 140 + ... = ...

246 − 73 = ...

$$100 + 140 + 6$$
$$-70 + 3$$

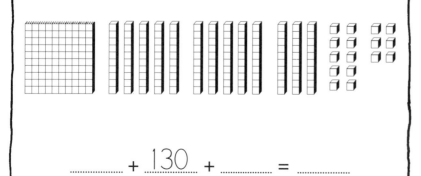

.... + 130 + ... = ...

246 − 78 = ...

$$100 + 130 + 16$$
$$-70 + 8$$

Developing column subtraction
(Follows *Giant Discussion Book* page 34.)

Name ....

MRS BARKER'S BAKERY
Muffin prices

| Singles | Twin-pack | Four-pack | Six-pack |
| 45p | 85p | £1.60 | £2.20 |

1. How much would you save by buying a pack rather than single muffins?

Number of muffins	Cost of singles	Cost of a pack	Saving
2	45 x 2 = ... p	85p	.... – 85 = ... p
4			
6			

2. Solve these problems. (Each time, pretend you have £5.)

How many twin-packs could you buy?	How many four-packs could you buy?	What is the greatest number of muffins you could buy?
....	....	
How much change would you get?	How much change would you get?	
....	....	....

Name ....

Colour the labels that match the amount in the jugs.

500 ml	2.5 l
	250 ml
	$\frac{1}{4}$ l
	0.25 l

I litre	$\frac{3}{4}$ l
	0.75 l
	750 ml
	75 ml

750 ml	0.5 l
	$\frac{1}{2}$ l
	500 ml
	5000 ml

2 litres / I litre	$1\frac{1}{4}$ l
	1.25 l
	1250 ml
	125 ml

2l / Il	750 ml
	1.75 ml
	1750 ml
	$1\frac{3}{4}$ l

5l / 4l / 3l / 2l / Il	2500 l
	$2\frac{1}{2}$ l
	250 l
	2.5 l

Working with fractions of a litre
(Follows *Giant Discussion Book* page 36.)

Name ....

1. Make ticks (✓) in the table to show each combination.

	BERRY 200ml	Tropical Fruit 250ml	ORANGE 300ml	Pineapple 500ml	APPLE 750ml
2 different juices that make $\frac{1}{2}$ litre altogether.	✓		✓		
2 different juices that make 1 litre altogether.					
2 different juices that make $\frac{3}{4}$ litre altogether.					
3 different juices that make 1 litre altogether.					
3 different juices that make $1\frac{1}{2}$ litres altogether.					
4 different juices that make $1\frac{1}{4}$ litres altogether.					
4 different juices that make $1\frac{3}{4}$ litres altogether.					

2. For these problems, write an answer for each juice.

How much less than 1 litre is in the container?	800 ml				
How many times could the container fill a 50 ml measure?	4				
How many containers make $1\frac{1}{2}$ litres?	$7\frac{1}{2}$				

Solving real-life problems: measurement
(Follows *Giant Discussion Book* page 37.)

Name ....

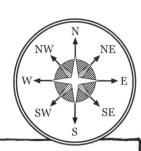

I. Follow the compass directions to draw each picture.
(Start from → each time.)

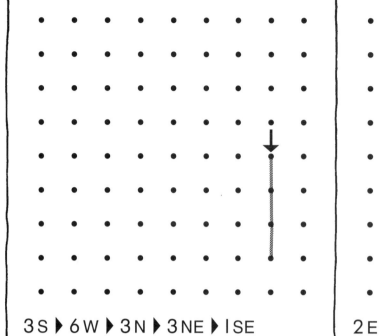

3S ▶ 6W ▶ 3N ▶ 3NE ▶ ISE
IN ▶ IE ▶ 2S ▶ ISE

2E ▶ INE ▶ 2E ▶ ISW ▶ 2S ▶ ISE
2W ▶ INW ▶ 2W ▶ INW ▶ INE

2. Write the compass directions for these.

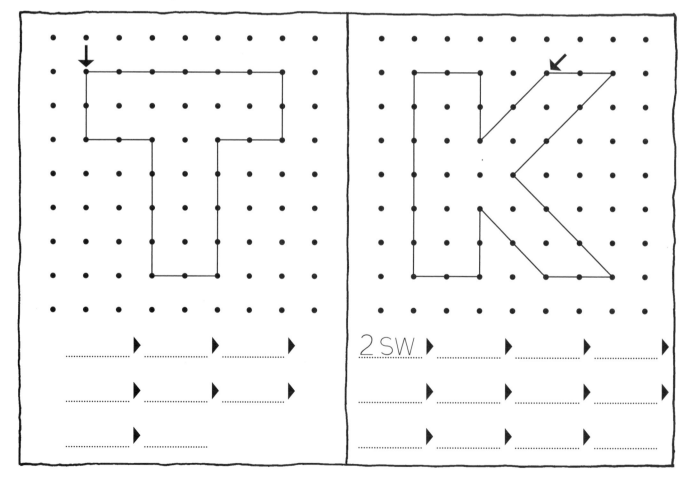

.... ▶ .... ▶ .... ▶

.... ▶ .... ▶ .... ▶

.... ▶

2 SW ▶ .... ▶ .... ▶ .... ▶

.... ▶ .... ▶ .... ▶

.... ▶ .... ▶ .... ▶

Name ....

Cut out the .
Attach it to the compass with a 📌.
(Match the ⊕ marks.)

✂

1. Start with the ➡ pointing East each time.
   Give each of these turns in degrees.
   (Use the multiples of 45 to help.)

Clockwise turns	
from **E** to **S**	°
from **E** to **W**	°
from **E** to **NW**	°
Anti-clockwise turns	
from **E** to **N**	°
from **E** to **NW**	°
from **E** to **SW**	°

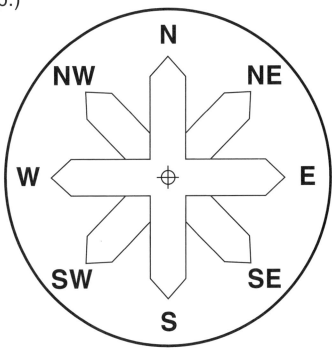

Multiples of 45			
45	90	135	180
225	270	315	360

2. Start with the ➡ pointing East each time.
   Make the turn and write the new direction.

clockwise 90°	anti-clockwise 45° ....
clockwise 135°	anti-clockwise 270° ....
clockwise 315°	anti-clockwise 225° ....

Teacher's note:
Copy this sheet on to light cardboard.
Provide round-head fasteners.

Describing angles in turns and degrees
(Follows *Giant Discussion Book* page 39.)

Name ....

Use the pictures to help multiply.
Write the missing numbers to show each step.

14 × 9

= (10 × 9) + (4 × 9)

= 90 + ...

= ....

	10	4
9	90	

13 × 8

= (.......... × 8) + (.......... × 8)

= .... + ...

= ....

	10	3
8	....	....

24 × 9

= (.......... × ....) + (.......... × ....)

= .... + ...

= ....

	20	4
9	....	....

29 × 7

= (.......... × ....) + (.......... × ....)

= .... + ...

= ....

	20	9
7	....	....

Understanding the distributive law
(Follows *Giant Discussion Book* page 40.)

Solve each problem. Show your working.

 LEMONS 72

 PEACHES 78

 ORANGES 84

 APPLES 96

Four families shared a box of lemons. How many lemons did each family get?	The apples were divided among 4 bags. How many apples were in each bag?
The peaches were packed into 6 trays. How many peaches were on each tray?	Suppose the apples were for a 6-day camp. How many apples per day is that?
A café used a box of oranges in 3 days. How many oranges per day was that?	What is 72 divided by 3?

Name ....

Postcard Prices

80p each   95p each   £1.20 each

6 cards   4 cards   5 cards

£4.50   £3.00   £4.00

Try to write number sentences to show the steps you used.

Solve these problems.

How much would 4 single cost?	Tom bought 24 in packets of 6. How many packets was that?	How many packets of could you buy with £20?
How much cheaper is a packet of 4?	What was the total cost?	How many cards is that?
How many packets of 4 could be filled from 32 ?	What is the cost of each in a packet?	Jasmine wants 30 postcards. How much cheaper is it to buy packets of rather than packets of ?
How much would those packets cost altogether?	How much more is one single postcard?	

Name ....

For each row of sweets:
- colour some of the sweets **green** to match the first label
- colour the other sweets **red**
- write numbers to make the other two labels **true**.

One in every 4 sweets is **green.**

.... in every 4 sweets are **red**.

For every .... **green** sweets there are .... **red** sweets.

2 in every 5 sweets are **green.**

.... in every .... sweets are **red**.

For every .... **green** sweets there are .... **red** sweets.

3 in every 4 sweets are **green.**

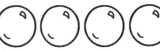

.... in every .... sweets is **red**.

For every .... **green** sweets there is .... **red** sweet.

Name ....

Complete the missing parts of each puzzle.

Make sure you include a fraction and a decimal for each puzzle.

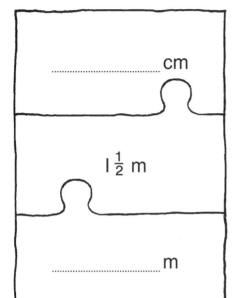

.... cm

$1\frac{1}{2}$ m

.... m

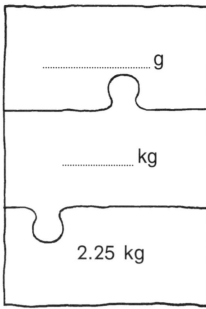

.... g

.... kg

2.25 kg

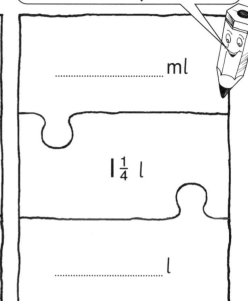

.... ml

$1\frac{1}{4}$ l

.... l

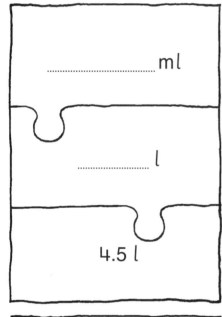

.... ml

.... l

4.5 l

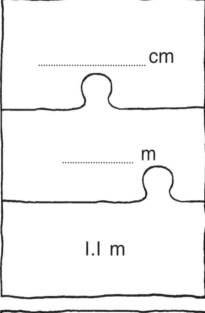

.... cm

.... m

1.1 m

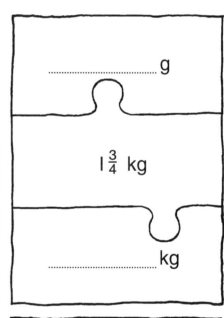

.... g

$1\frac{3}{4}$ kg

.... kg

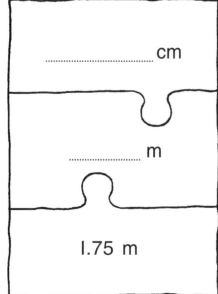

.... cm

.... m

1.75 m

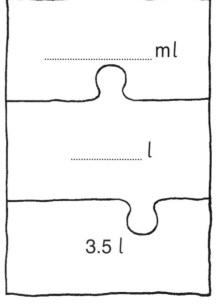

.... ml

.... l

3.5 l

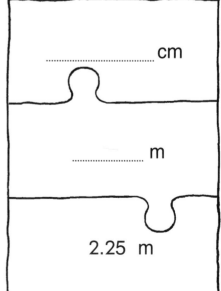

.... cm

.... m

2.25 m

Recognising the equivalence of decimals and fractions
(Follows *Giant Discussion Book* page 44.)

Name ....

Flights departing from London

Departs London	Arrives Glasgow	Departs London	Arrives Aberdeen
6:00 a.m.	7:25 a.m.	6:00 a.m.	7:35 a.m.
6:45 a.m.	8:05 a.m.	8:55 a.m.	9:25 a.m.
7:15 a.m.	8:35 a.m.	11:05 a.m.	12:35 p.m.
10:55 a.m.	12:15 p.m.	2:00 p.m.	3:30 p.m.
1:40 p.m.	3:00 p.m.	3:50 p.m.	5:20 p.m.
5:05 p.m.	6:25 p.m.	5:10 p.m.	6:40 p.m.
6:40 p.m.	8:00 p.m.	6:40 p.m.	8:10 p.m.
7:15 p.m.	8:35 p.m.	7:55 p.m.	9:25 p.m.

1. Write the departure time for these flights.

The first flight leaving London after 4 p.m.	The flight leaving London closest to noon.	The flight that arrives in Glasgow at 8:35 a.m.	The flight that arrives in Aberdeen at 9:25 p.m.
....	....	....	....

2. How long are these flights?

The 6:00 a.m. to Glasgow. .... hr .... mins	The 8:55 a.m. to Aberdeen.	Afternoon flights to Glasgow.	Evening flights to Aberdeen. ....

3. At what time would you leave London so that you would arrive in:

Glasgow by 9:00 a.m.?	Glasgow by 5:30 p.m.?	Aberdeen by 11 a.m.?	Aberdeen by 12:30 p.m.?
....	....	....	....

Name ....

Swimming Pool Opening Hours

Pool Open	***Family Night**	***Pool Closed**
7:30 a.m. to 8:00 p.m. every day (except *).	Every Tuesday 6:00 p.m. to 10:30 p.m.	1st and 3rd Monday each month.

1. Use the calendar to find these dates for June.
   Figure out the dates for July.

Family Nights

June	July

June						
S	M	T	W	T	F	S
				1	2	3
4	5	6	7	8	9	10
11	12	13	14	15	16	17
18	19	20	21	22	23	24
25	26	27	28	29	30	

Days the Pool is Closed

June	July

2. For how many hours is the pool open:

   on Wednesdays? .... on Tuesdays? ....

3. Solve these problems.

Stewart swam from 7:18 until 8:05. How long was that?	Jessica swam for 40 minutes. She stopped at 5:15. What time did she start?	Ben swam for 45 minutes. He started at 8:50. What time did he stop?
....	....	....

Name ....

1. Write each of these numbers on the correct part of the Carroll diagram.

125 115

121 151

150 152

101 105

110 112

Numbers		
	Less than 120	**120 or more**
Even		
Odd		

2. Draw and colour the following shapes on the Carroll diagram.

- a red triangle
- a blue triangle
- a green triangle

- a red square
- a blue square
- a green square

- a red rectangle
- a blue rectangle
- a green rectangle

- some other shapes of your choice

Shapes		
	Quadrilaterals	**Not Quadrilaterals**
Red		
Not Red		

Using a Carroll diagram to classify data
(Follows *Giant Discussion Book* page 47.)

47

Name ....

1. Write each of these numbers in the correct 'bin'.

31 27 75 30 100 96

20 36 80 29 45

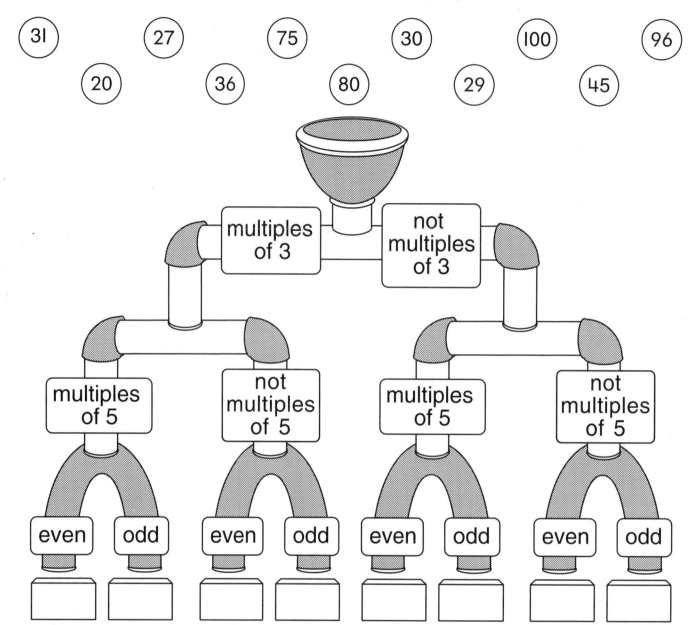

2. For each of the two empty bins above:
   • list the labels along the path to that bin
   • write 2 or 3 numbers that would end up in that bin.

Path:	_not mutiples of 3_	Path:	
Numbers:		Numbers:	